# JOUR
# THE PYRAMIDS

by Mark Falstein
illustrated by Anne Olds

### CHAPTERS

**Harcourt**

Orlando   Boston   Dallas   Chicago   San Diego

Visit *The Learning Site!*
**www.harcourtschool.com**

**Journey by Truck**

By now Candace Moore was used to the bouncing. The truck was moving along at 25 miles per hour, but the paved road had ended many miles back. They were following the tracks of other traffic along the Nile River.

"We could take the train," Uncle Leo had told Candace. "But it's always crowded, and it's not very reliable. That's why Anwar is driving passengers by truck. This is the best way to travel through Kush, unless you want to go the old-fashioned way—by camel."

"Kush?" Candace asked, grinning at her uncle. "I thought it's been called Nubia for the last seventeen centuries."

"True," said Uncle Leo. "But any time I come here, I feel as if I'm going back to ancient times."

Uncle Leo was an archaeologist. He had led digs all over Africa. He had invited Candace to spend part of her vacation working with him at Meroë [mer´e•wē´].

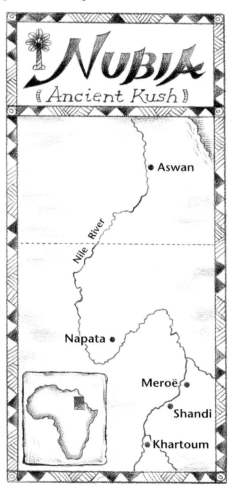

"It almost rhymes with 'narrow way,'" she had told her mother. "The kings of Kush ruled there for about 600 years. They were buried in pyramids, like in Egypt. I can't wait to see the pyramids!"

Uncle Leo had sent Candace a plane ticket to Khartoum, Sudan. There he had met her with the truck he had hired.

"Meroë is pretty isolated now, but it was once the capital of a great kingdom," Uncle Leo said. "The important buildings were made of stone brought there from quarries. Because it's in the desert, it has been well preserved."

"Why is that?" Candace asked.

"The desert is very hot and dry," her uncle said. "There is no water to get into cracks and cause the stone to break apart."

Anwar nodded. "We get only about an inch (2.5 cm) of rain during the whole year. In the summer, the temperature averages about 110° Fahrenheit (45° C)."

"Wow!" said Candace. "That is hot and dry!"

"Working in the digs here is hard work," Uncle Leo said. "Still, it's exciting. Many archaeologists have worked in Meroë, but there's still a lot to discover."

"We're getting near Shandi," said Anwar. "Shall we show Kandake the ruins?"

"Sure, why not?" said Uncle Leo.

"Are there pyramids in the ruins?" Candace asked.

"No," her uncle said, "but you'll see them soon!"

### A Puzzling Building

Soon they stopped at an ancient building that seemed to be falling apart.

"Kush was once a great trading nation," Uncle Leo explained. "Kushite traders carried gold, ivory, and rare wood to Egypt from other parts of Africa. Later, Greek and Roman traders came here, too. This building looks as if it were put together from parts of Egyptian, Greek, and Roman temples."

"Was it a temple?" Candace asked.

"No one knows. One archaeologist called it a kiosk, and now that's what everyone calls it."

"This building is like no other building in the world," said Uncle Leo. Inside the ruin were rooms, courtyards, and passageways. Pictures of elephants were carved on the outer wall.

"We don't know what this place was used for," said Uncle Leo. "It may have been a temple or a palace. Or, it may have been a cattle market or a stopping place for travelers. A lot of animal bones have been found here, but no tombs."

Candace stared at the enormous ruin. To her it looked like a royal palace. The entrance ramps looked big enough to have been passageways for elephants.

**3800 B.C.**
**First Trading Culture**
**in Nubia**

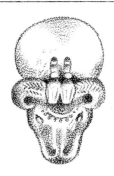

"Uncle Leo," Candace asked, "If Kush was so important, how come so little is known about it?"

"Good question," said her uncle. "It's because no one today can read the Kushitic language. At first, the people of Kush used the Egyptian form of writing. They were often at war with Egypt, but they also borrowed a great deal of their culture from the Egyptians.

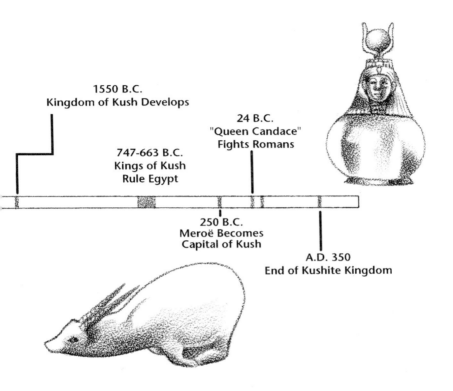

**1550 B.C.**
**Kingdom of Kush Develops**

**747-663 B.C.**
**Kings of Kush**
**Rule Egypt**

**24 B.C.**
**"Queen Candace"**
**Fights Romans**

**250 B.C.**
**Meroë Becomes**
**Capital of Kush**

**A.D. 350**
**End of Kushite Kingdom**

"Around 750 B.C., the kings of Kush actually took over Egypt. They ruled as Egypt's twenty-fifth dynasty. But then they were driven back to their capital, Napata. Later they moved the capital farther south to Meroë, on the banks of the Nile River.

"By then the people of Kush had stopped imitating the Egyptians. Their culture developed in new ways. They invented their own ingenious alphabet. It had twenty-three letters."

### A Lost Language

"We know how the letters were pronounced," Uncle Leo explained, "but we don't know what the words mean. No one speaks the Kush language today."

He pulled a sheet of paper out of his pocket and handed it to her. On it, Candace saw the letters of the Kush alphabet, along with the way each one was pronounced. The letters were nothing like English letters.

"I can see why the Kush language is so hard to translate!" she said.

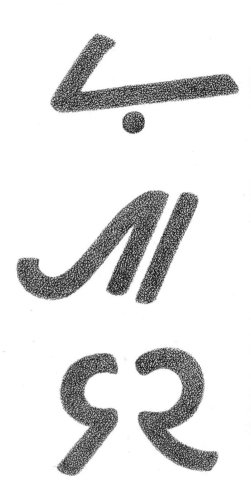

That night Candace and Uncle Leo stayed in a guest house in the market town of Shandi. "The kings of Kush built stone palaces," Candace commented. "So why do the Nubians of today build with mud bricks?"

"Because we are not kings, Kandake," Anwar said. "Ordinary people cannot have stones brought here from quarries. It was the same in those times. We build with what we have—good old Nile River mud."

"It makes cool, comfortable houses," Uncle Leo added. "They just don't stay preserved for us archaeologists to find."

**Pyramids at Last!**

The next afternoon they reached the site of Meroë. Dozens of pyramids covered the ground. They were steeper than the pyramids of Egypt but not nearly as tall.

"At last!" said Candace. Then she frowned. "Why are some of them flat on top?" she asked.

"They weren't always flat," Uncle Leo told her. "Over the centuries, the tops of some of them have crumbled. Stones from the tops have fallen into the center."

Not far away was an area marked off by ropes.

"That's our dig," said Uncle Leo. "Meroë is not exactly a new site. But it's so isolated that it has not been explored nearly as well as sites in Egypt. There's still plenty to find here, even though many of these tombs were robbed centuries ago. Thieves stole much of the gold and other precious things that the Kushites had buried in their pyramids."

"What kinds of things do you think we'll find?" Candace asked. She could already feel the desert heat beating down on her head.

"Some day," Anwar said, "someone may dig up a stone with a long written passage in both Egyptian and Nubian. Then some ingenious scholar will be able to translate our ancient language. Perhaps it will be you, Kandake."

"Anwar, why do you keep calling me 'con-*dah*-kay'? You know my name is Candace." Candace thought she was being teased.

"Don't you know?" asked Anwar with a grin. "Professor, why don't you tell her?"

"You see, Kandake—*Candace*," said her uncle, "*Kandake* was the word for *queen* in the language of Kush. Around 24 B.C. the Roman Empire tried to take over Kush. A queen led the army that stopped their advance. A Roman writer called her *Candace* in a book he wrote. He didn't know the word meant 'queen.' He thought it was her name."

"That's why a lot of American girls and women are named Candace," said Uncle Leo. "That's where your name came from."

"Well!" said Candace. "You and Anwar may call me 'queen' or the name of a queen, just as long as you treat me like one!"

The two men laughed. "All right, my lady," Uncle Leo said. "Tomorrow at 6:00 A.M., the queen needs to be up and ready to start work!"